唧唧，喳喳，嗡嗡，呼呼

Chirp, chirp, churr, churr, buzz, buzz, whirr, whirr.

樹葉沙沙，吊牀搖擺。啪啪，嚓嚓，孩子們在玩耍。

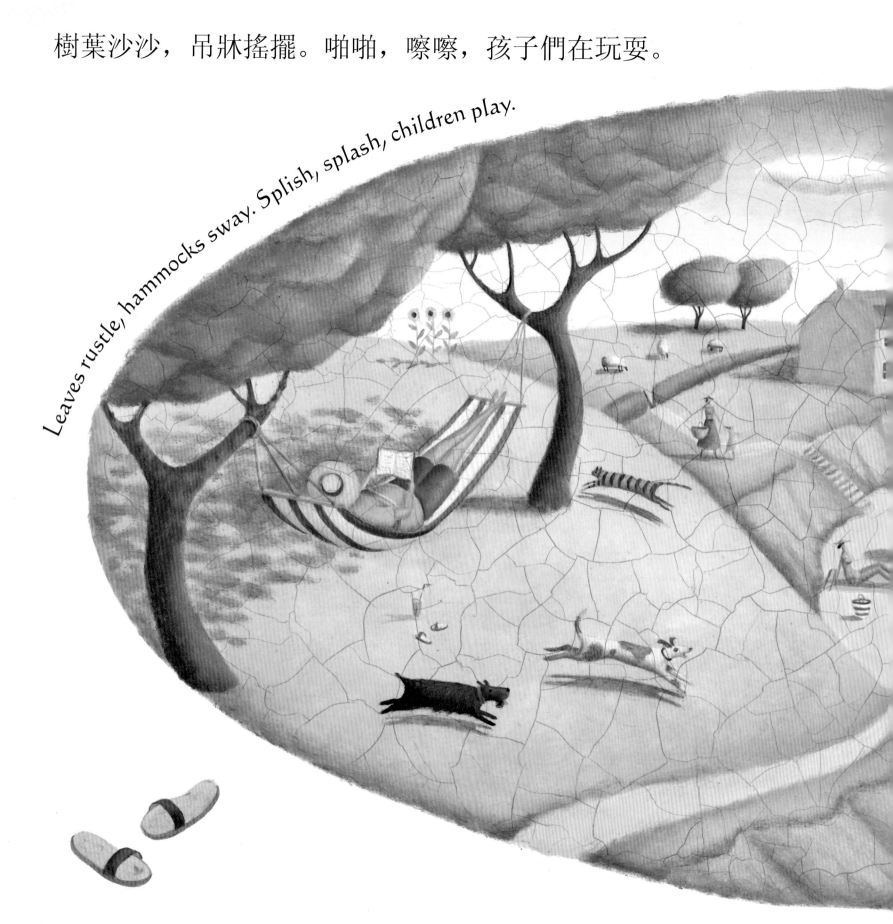

Leaves rustle, hammocks sway. Splish, splash, children play.

浮雲飄動，狗兒奔跑。嗞嗞，嗞嗞，夏日陽光在閃耀。

Clouds drift, dogs run. Sizzle, sizzle, summer sun.

聽聽，聽聽⋯ 夏天走了。再見小蟲子，秋天來了。

Listen, listen ... summer's gone.
Good-bye insects, autumn's come.

噗嗵，噗嗵，橡樹果子掉落。快啊，快啊，松鼠跳躍。

Plop, plop, acorns drop.
Hurry, scurry, squirrels hop.

快啊，快啊，南瓜熟了。摘啊，摘啊，蘋果，玉米。

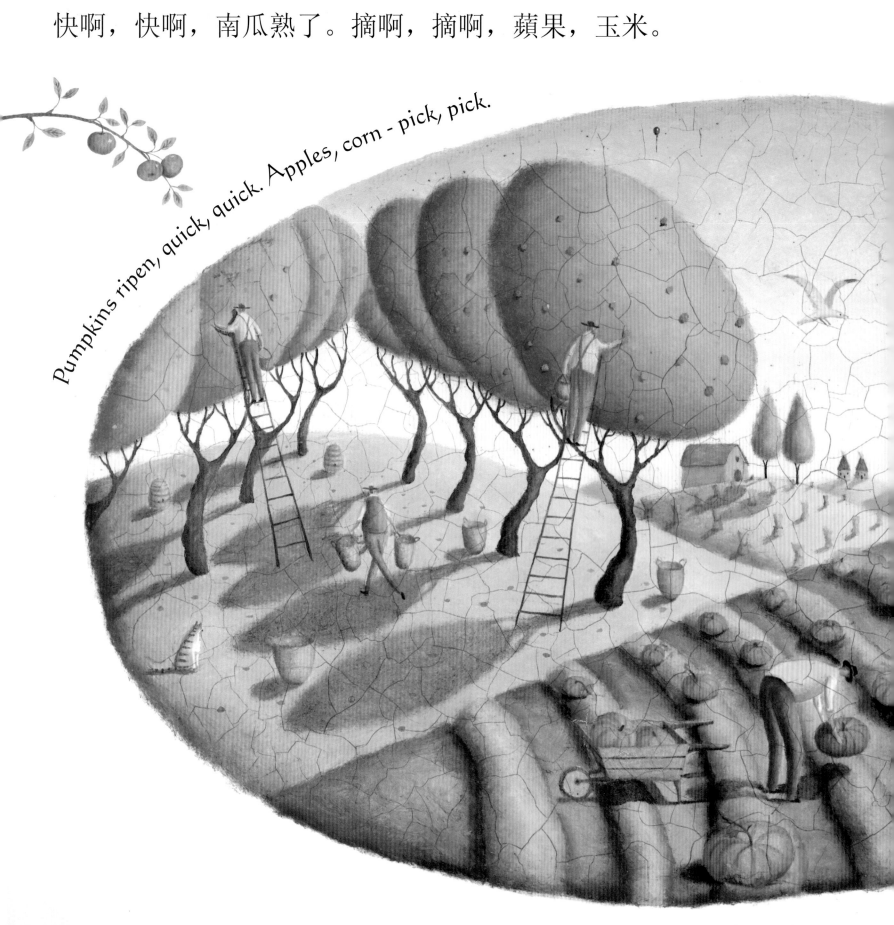

Pumpkins ripen, quick, quick. Apples, corn - pick, pick.

嘎吱，嘎吱，人們走動。喔喔，喔喔，海鷗鳴叫。

Crunch, crunch, people walk. Aak, aak, seagulls squawk.

哦哦，哦哦，雁兒們鳴叫。嗖嗖，嗖嗖，樹葉落下。

Honk, honk, geese call. Swish, swish, leaves fall.

噓噓，噓噓，帽子飛翔。嗚嗚，嗚嗚，貓頭鷹嗚咽。

Whoosh, whoosh, hats fly. Whoo, whoo, owls cry.

聽聽，聽聽⋯ 秋天走了。雪花細說：「冬天很好玩。」

Listen, listen … autumn's gone. Snowflakes whisper, "Winter's fun."

噓噓，噓噓，多雪的夜晚。雪花閃爍，潔白光亮。

Shhh, shhh, snowy night. Snow sparkles, white, bright.

嘎嚓，嘎嚓，靴子踏步。成人們剷雪，孩子們嬉戲。

Crunch, crunch, boots clomp. Grown-ups shovel, children romp.

溜冰的人旋轉，滑雪的人滑翔。吱，呼，滑倒，滑行。

Skaters spin, skiers glide. Zip, zoom, slip, slide.

呵呵，呵呵，熱身時間。噢噢，哦哦，蠟燭閃耀。

Brrr, brrr, warm-up time. Ooh, aah, candles shine.

咕嚕，咕嚕，貓咪凝視。劈啪，劈啪，火焰燃燒。

Purr, purr, cats gaze. Crackle, crackle, fires blaze.

聽聽，聽聽⋯ 冬天走了。鳥兒鳴哨：「太陽出來了！」

Listen, listen ... winter's gone. Finches whistle, "Here's the sun!"

噗噗，噗噗，球莖萌芽，樹葉生長，花兒吶喊。

Pop, pop, bulbs sprout. Leaves grow, flowers shout.

咯嚓，咯嚓，小雞們孵化。偷偷看，偷偷看，小雞們抓地。

Crick, crack, babies hatch. Peep, peep, chickens scratch.

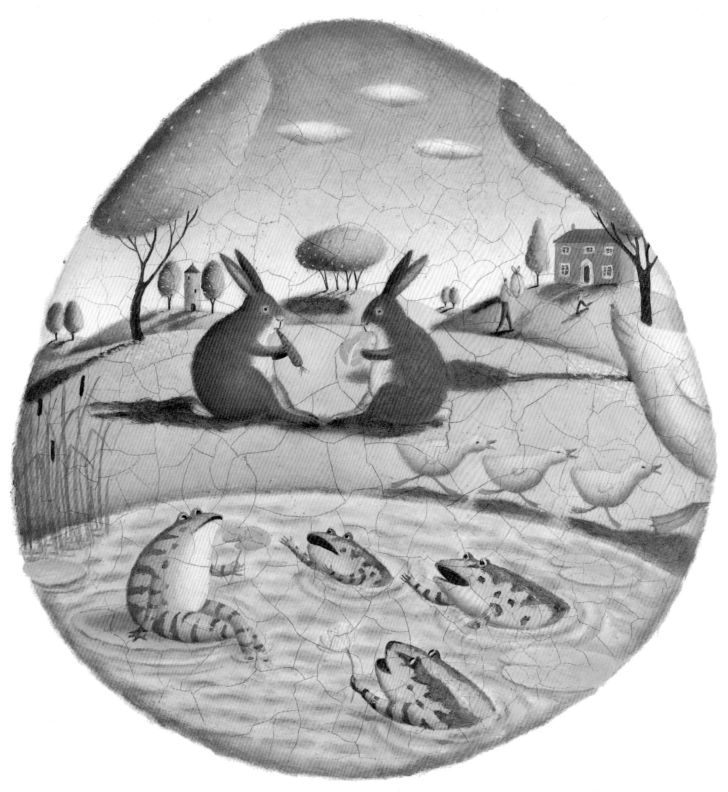

青蛙呱呱，小鴨子嘎嘎。咬呀，咬呀，小兔子嘴嚼美食。

Frogs croak, ducklings quack. Munch, munch, rabbits snack.

啪嗒，啪嗒，雨珠落下。嘰嘰，喳喳，麻雀聚集。

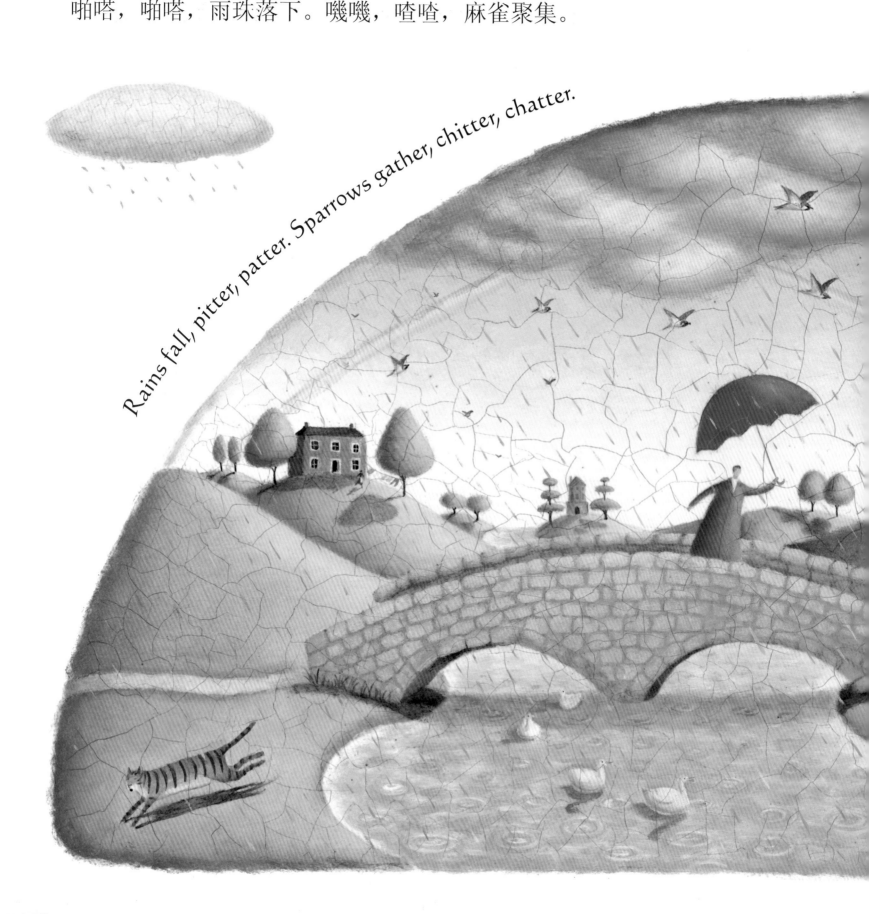

Rains fall, pitter, patter. Sparrows gather, chitter, chatter.

聽聽，聽聽… 春天走了，新的季節開始了。

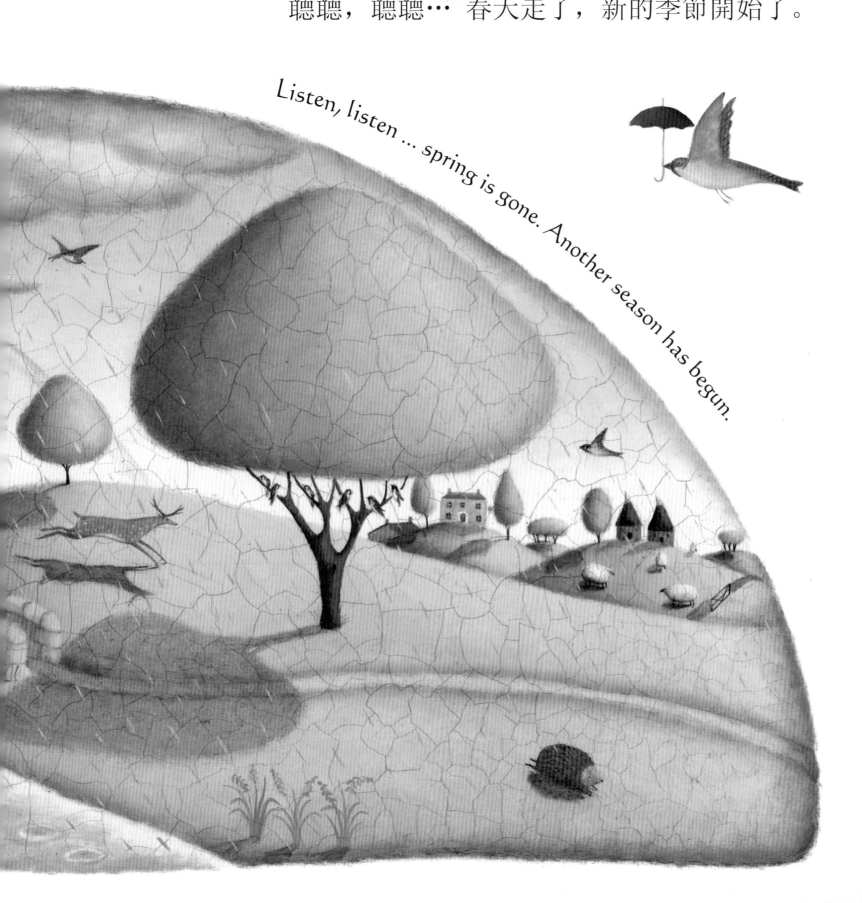

Listen, listen ... spring is gone. Another season has begun.

在空中，在地上，白天和黑夜… 那是什麼聲音呢？

In the air, on the ground, night and day - what's that sound?

聽聽，聽聽⋯ 春天過後，夏天來臨⋯

Listen, listen ... after spring, summer comes and ...

昆蟲都在歌唱！

Insects sing!

唧唧，喳喳，嗡嗡，呼呼。

Chirp, chirp, churr, churr, buzz, buzz, whirr, whirr.

In the summer, can you see

a cricket

a butterfly

a mosquito

a bee

a dragonfly

a grasshopper

a beetle

a sunflower

a daisy

a leaf?

In the autumn, can you see

an owl

a goose

an acorn

an apple

a squirrel

a stalk of wheat

a pumpkin

an ear of corn

a seagull

a leaf?

In the winter, can you see

a crow

a mouse

a starling

a paw print

a holly berry

an icicle

a snowflake

a leaf?

a sprig of mistletoe

In the spring, can you see

a tulip

a daffodil

a bluebell

a sparrow

a rainbow

a rabbit

a frog

a duckling

a chick

a leaf?

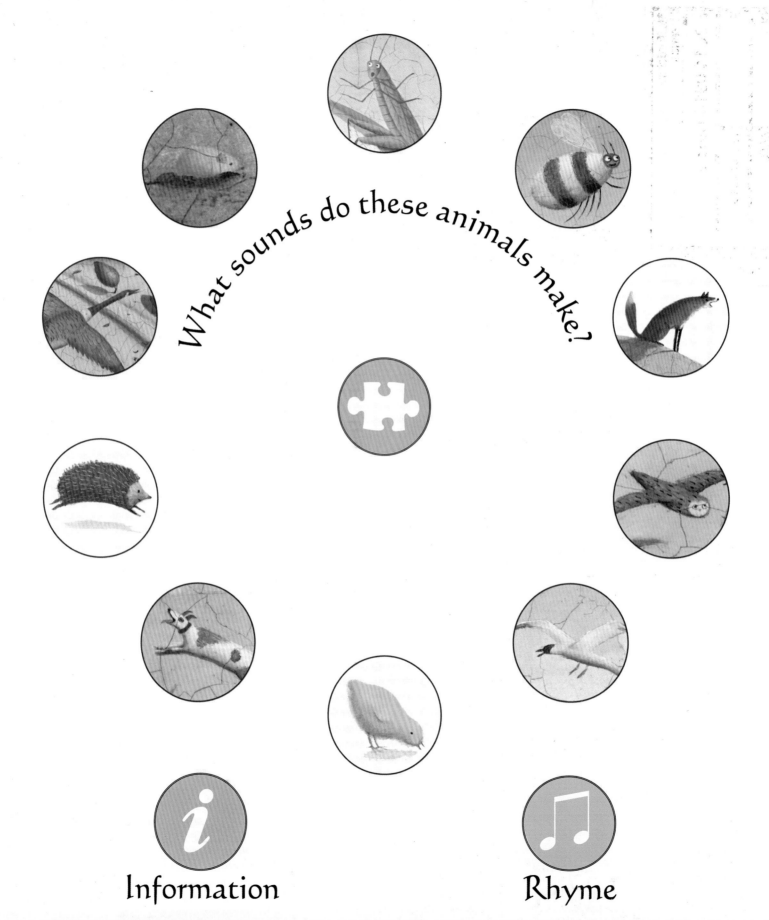

What sounds do these animals make?

Information

Rhyme